STING

THE ANT...

THE DEFINITIVE
COLLECTION

WISE PUBLICATIONS
LONDON / NEW YORK / SYDNEY

EXCLUSIVE DISTRIBUTORS:

MUSIC SALES LIMITED
8/9 FRITH STREET, LONDON W1V 5TZ,
ENGLAND

MUSIC SALES PTY LIMITED
120 ROTHSCHILD AVENUE, ROSEBERY, NSW 2018,
AUSTRALIA

THIS BOOK © COPYRIGHT 1991 BY
WISE PUBLICATIONS
ORDER NO.AM85259
ISBN 0.7119.2703.0

DESIGNED BY MICHAEL BELL DESIGN
COMPILED BY PETER EVANS
TYPESET BY CAPITAL SETTERS
PHOTOGRAPHS BY BRIAN ARIS

MUSIC SALES' COMPLETE CATALOGUE
LISTS THOUSANDS OF TITLES AND IS FREE FROM
YOUR LOCAL MUSIC SHOP, OR DIRECT FROM
MUSIC SALES LIMITED

PLEASE SEND A CHEQUE/POSTAL ORDER
FOR £1.50 FOR POSTAGE TO:
MUSIC SALES LIMITED,
NEWMARKET ROAD, BURY ST. EDMUNDS,
SUFFOLK IP33 3YB

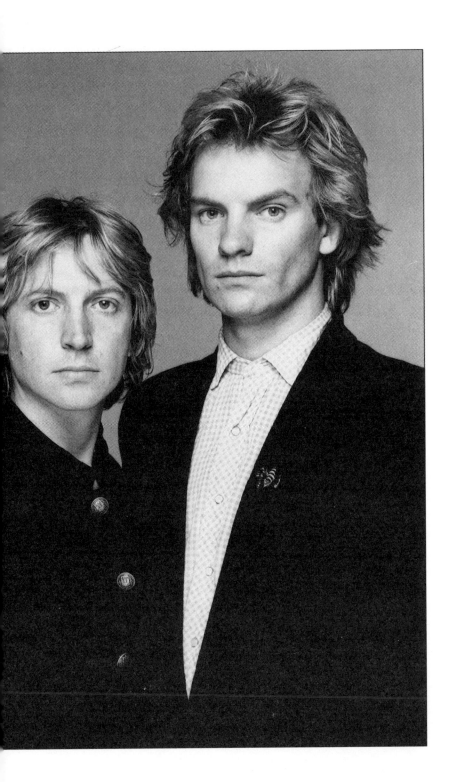

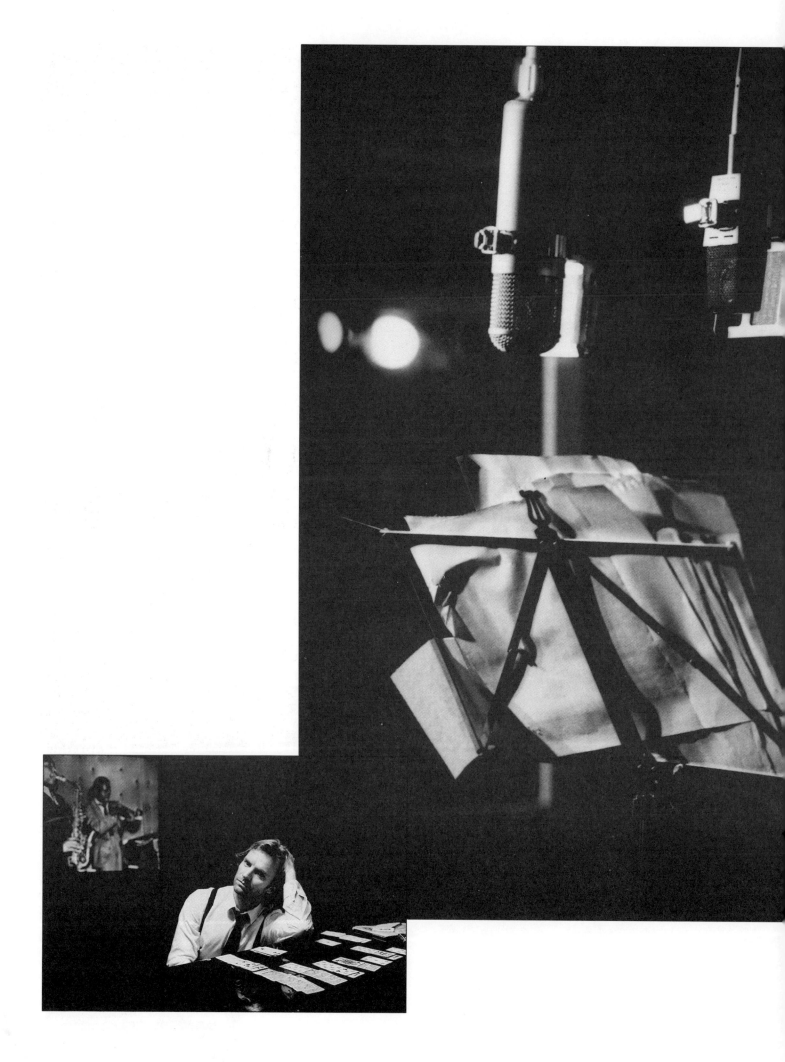

CAN'T STAND LOSING YOU

WORDS & MUSIC BY STING

Steady beat

called you so man-y times to-day___ and I guess it's all true what your
see you've sent my let-ters back___ and my L.___ P. rec-ords and

girl friends say that you don't ev-er want to see me a-gain___ and your
they're all scratched I can't see the point in a-noth-er day___ when

broth-er's gon-na kill me and he's six foot ten I guess you'd call it cow-ar-dice___ but I'm
no-bod-y list-ens to a word I say you can call it lack of con-fi-dence___ but to
guess you'd call it su-i-cide___ but

not pre-pared to go on___ like this___ I ___ can't I can't I can't stand los-ing, I ___
car - ry on liv-ing does-n't make no sense___
I'm too full to swal-low___ my pride___

___ can't I can't I can't stand los-ing, I ___ can't I can't I can't I can't stand los - ing___

___ you___ I can't stand los - ing you___ I can't stand los -

-ing you___ I can't stand los - ing you._____ I

can't stand los-ing I ___ can't I can't I can't stand los-ing I ___ can't I can't I

7

SO LONELY

WORDS & MUSIC BY STING

ROXANNE
WORDS & MUSIC BY STING

MESSAGE IN A BOTTLE

WORDS & MUSIC BY STING

Res - cue me __ be - fore I fall __ in - to __ des - pair __ o __
Love _ can mend _ your life __ but love __ can break your heart __
hun - dred bil - lion cast - a - ways __ look - ing for __ a home __

I'll send __ an S. __ O. __ S. __ to the world __ I'll send __ an S. __ O. __ S. __ to the world

__ I hope __ that some - one gets __ my, I hope that some - one gets __ my,

I hope __ that some - one gets __ my __ mes - sage in a bot - tle __ yeah.

mes - sage in a bot - tle __ yeah.

WALKING ON THE MOON

WORDS & MUSIC BY STING

some say ... to - mor - row's an - oth - er day_

you'll stay ... I may as well play

Keep it up ... keep it up

DON'T STAND SO CLOSE TO ME

WORDS & MUSIC BY STING

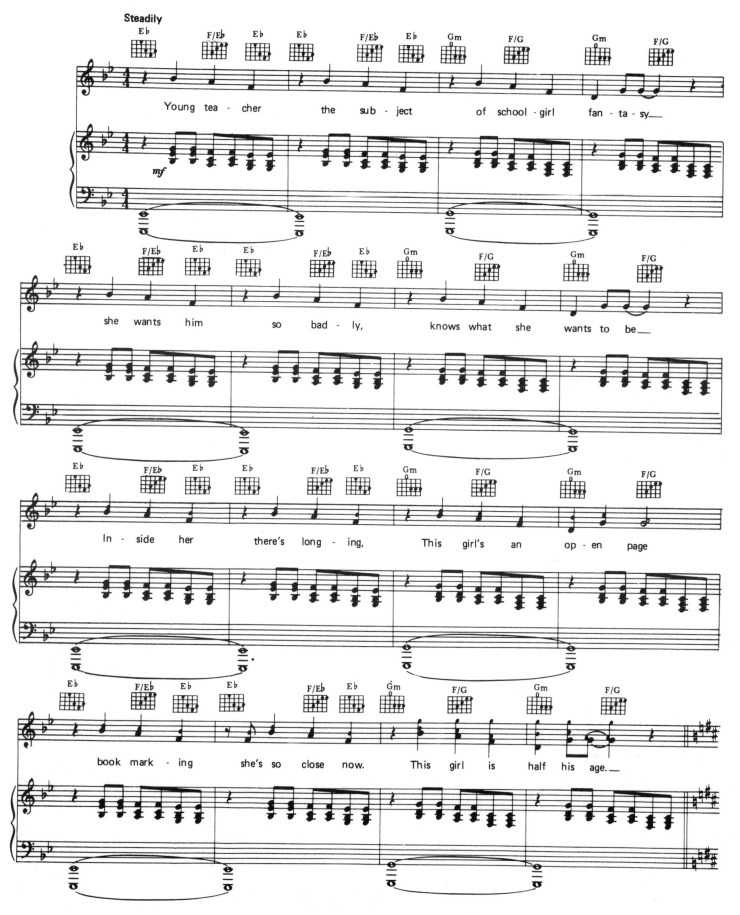

Don't stand   don't stand so   don't stand so   close to me—   don't stand

don't stand so   don't stand so   close to me.—

℁ = Instrumental

Her   friends are—   so   jea - lous   you know how bad   girls ___ get—
Loose   talk — in —   the   class - room   to   hurt they   try   and___   try—

Some - times   it's   not so   ea - sy   to   be   the   tea - cher's ___ pet.—
Strong   words   in   the   staff room   the   ac - cu - sa - tions___ fly,—

Temp - ta - tion   frus - tra - tion   so bad it   makes   him ___ cry—
it's   no   use   he   sees   her   he starts   to   shake and___ cough—

BRING ON THE NIGHT

WORDS & MUSIC BY STING

25

DRIVEN TO TEARS

WORDS & MUSIC BY STING

VERSE 2: Hide my face in my hands, shame wells in my throat,
My comfortable existence is reduced to a shallow meaningless party,
Seems that when some innocent die,
All we can offer them is a page in some magazine
Too many cameras and not enough food,
'Cause this is what we've seen.

CHORUS: *(Repeat)*

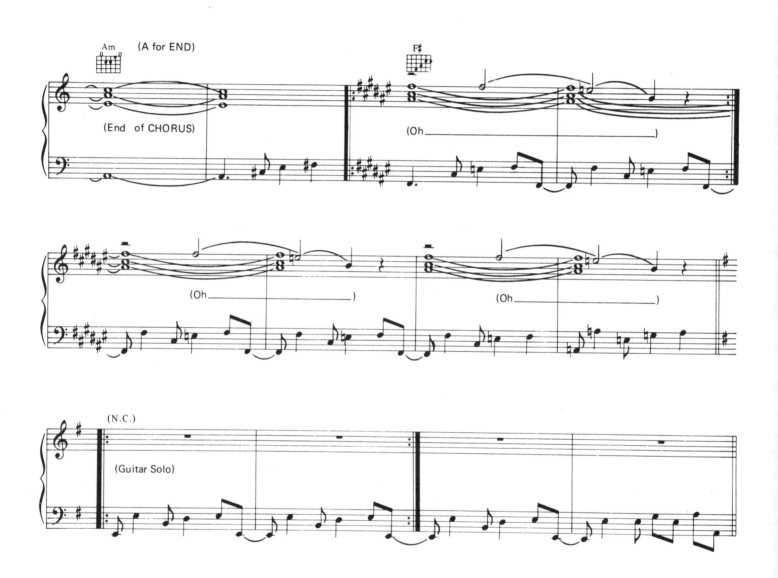

VERSE 3: Protest is futile, nothing seems to get through,
What's to become of our world, who knows what to do.
(½ Verse)

CHORUS: *Repeat — x 2*

VERSE & CHORUS: *(Instrumental)*

INVISIBLE SUN
WORDS & MUSIC BY STING

(Oh, oh, oh, ...)

1. I don't wanna spend the rest of my life___ look-ing at the bar-rel of an
2. I don't wanna spend my time in hell___ look-ing at the walls of a

Ar - ma - lite___ I don't wan-na spend the rest of my days___
pri - son cell___ I don't ev - er wan-na play the part___

- vi - si - ble sun___ it gives us hope when the whole day's done

VERSE 3: It's dark all day and it glows all night
Factory smoke and acetylene light
I face the day with my head caved in
Looking like something that the cat brought in.

CHORUS: (Repeat)

INSTRUMENTAL: (Repeat D/Bm9 chords) + Oh, oh, oh. . . . .

VERSE 4: And they're only gonna change this place
By killing everybody in the human race
And they would kill me for a cigarette
But I don't even wanna die just yet.

CHORUS: (Repeat)

INSTRUMENTAL: (Repeat) – to fade. + Oh, oh, oh. . . . .

EVERY LITTLE THING SHE DOES IS MAGIC

WORDS & MUSIC BY STING

1. Though I've tried be-fore_ to tell__ her of the feel- -ings I have for her in__ my_____ heart_____ ev-ery-time__ that I__ come near__ her I__ just lose__

VERSE 2: Do I have to tell the story
Of a thousand rainy days since we first met
It's a big enough umbrella
But it's always me that ends up getting wet.

CHORUS: (Repeat)

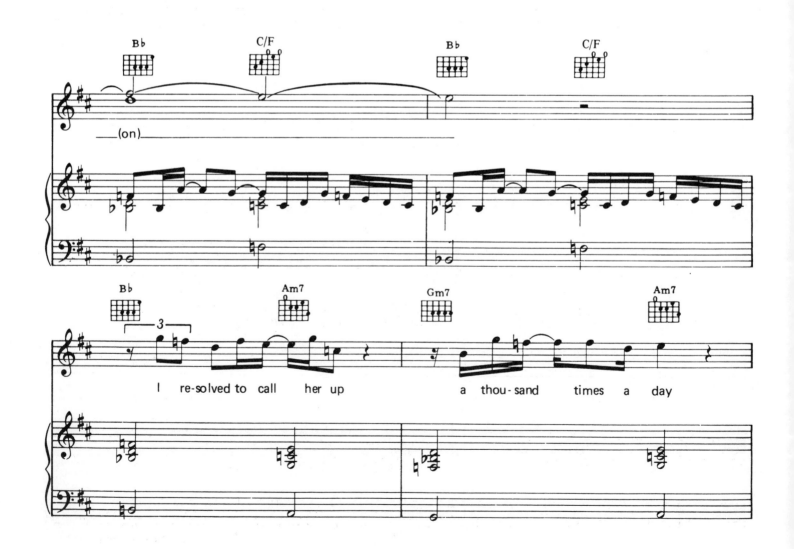

I re-solved to call her up   a thou-sand times a day

SPIRITS IN THE MATERIAL WORLD

WORDS & MUSIC BY STING

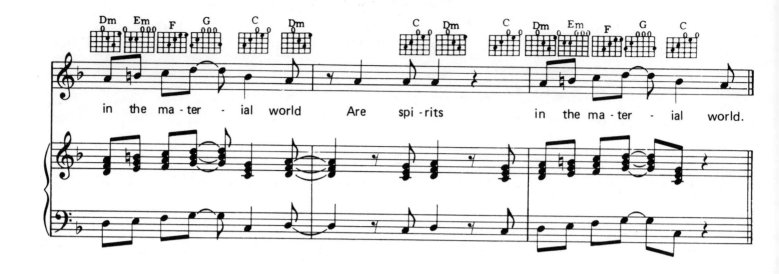

in the ma - ter - ial world   Are spi - rits   in the ma - ter - ial world.

VERSE 2: Our so-called leaders speak,
With words they try to jail you
They subjugate the meek
But it's the rhetoric of failure.

CHORUS: (Repeat)

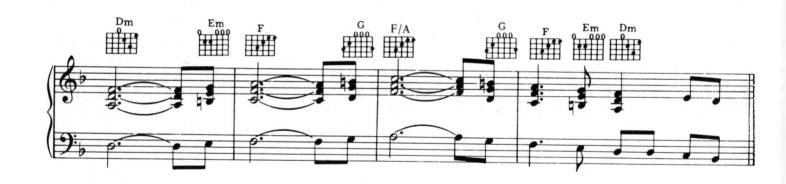

INTRO: (Repeat)

VERSE 3: Where does the answer lie?
Living from day to day
If it's something we can't buy
There must be another way

CHORUS: (Repeat) — to fade.

SYNCHRONICITY II

WORDS & MUSIC BY STING

40

there's on - ly so____ much more____ that he____ can____
lights.   Is a hu - mil - i - at - ing kick in the crotch
           The pain up - stairs____ that makes____ his eye - balls____

____ take____
____ ache____

Man - y miles__ a - way
Man - y miles__ a - way
Man - y miles__ a - way

some - thing crawls from the slime____ at the bot -
some - thing crawls to the sur - face____ of a dark
there's a shad - ow on the door____ of a cot -

- tom of a dark
____ Scot - tish lake
tage on the shore

Scot - tish lake

EVERY BREATH YOU TAKE

WORDS & MUSIC BY STING

Since you've gone__ I been lost____ with - out____ a trace, I dream at night I can on- -ly see__ your face. I look a - round but it's you I can't__ re - place, I feel so cold and I long for your__ em - brace. I keep cry - ing bab- -y bab - y please.____

48

WRAPPED AROUND YOUR FINGER

WORDS & MUSIC BY STING

Lyrics:

You con-sid-er me the young ap-
I have on-ly come here seek-ing know-

-pren-tice caught be-tween the Scyl-la and Char-
-ledge, things they would not teach me of in

IF YOU LOVE SOMEBODY SET THEM FREE

WORDS & MUSIC BY STING

59

RUSSIANS

WORDS & MUSIC BY STING

Medium slow and very steady

In Eu - rope and A - mer - i - ca there's a grow - ing feel - ing of hy - ste - ri - a. Con - di - tioned to re - spond to all the threats in the rhe - tor - i - cal speech - es of the

too.

There

Rus-sians love their child-ren too.

LOVE IS THE SEVENTH WAVE

WORDS & MUSIC BY STING

1 In the em-pire of ____ the sens - es you're the queen of all ____ you sur - vey;
2 Ev - 'ry rip - ple on ____ the o - cean ev - 'ry leaf on ev - 'ry tree,
(see additional lyrics for verses 3,4,5)

all the cit - ies, all ____ the na - tions, ev - 'ry - thing that falls ____ your way. I say,
ev - 'ry sand dune in the des - ert, ev - 'ry power we nev - er see. ____

3. Feel it rising in the cities,
   Feel it sweeping over land,
   Over borders, over frontiers;
   Nothing will it's power withstand I say,
   There is no deeper wave than this
   Rising in the world.
   There is no deeper wave than this.
   Listen to me, girl.

4. All the bloodshed, all the anger,
   All the weapons, all the greed,
   All the armies, all the missiles,
   All the symbols of our fear I say
   There is a deeper wave than this
   Rising in the world.
   There is a deeper wave than this.
   Listen to me, girl.

5. At the still point of destruction,
   At the centre of the fury;
   All the angels, all the devils
   All around us, can't you see?
   There is a deeper wave than this
   Rising in the land.
   There is a deeper wave than this,
   Nothing will withstand.

SHADOWS IN THE RAIN

WORDS & MUSIC BY STING

And I should heed_ my doc - tor's warn - ing.
It can't be an op - ti - cal_ il - lu - lu - sion.
I tell my friends_ there when_ I see_ them

He does the best_ with me_ he can._
How_ can you_
out - side_ my win - dow pane._

ex - plain

shad - ows in＿＿ the rain?

Shad - ows in＿＿ the rain.

last time To Coda ⊕

Sha - dows in＿＿ the rain.

Sha - dows in____ the rain.

D.C. al Coda
(Repeat verses 1 and 2)

CODA

Shad - ows in____ the rain.

Repeat ad lib. and Fade

Shad - ows in____ the rain.

73

WE WORK THE BLACK SEAM

WORDS & MUSIC BY STING

CONSIDER ME GONE

WORDS & MUSIC BY STING

in the house that we share, _____ but the space has been emp - tied _
shin - ing wa - ter's mud. Can - cer lurks deep
at war with my - self, the doc - tor has told me

of what - ev - er was there. There were cup - boards of pa - tience, _
in the sweet - est bud. Clouds and e - clip - ses
it's no good for my health. To search for per - fec - tion

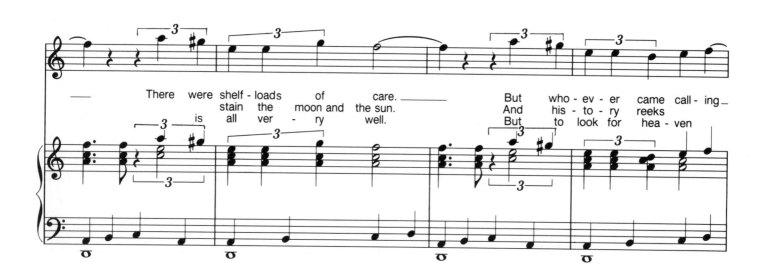

There were shelf - loads of care. _____ But who - ev - er came call - ing _
stain the moon and the sun. And his - to - ry reeks
is all ver - ry well. But to look for hea - ven

Dm7

con - sid - er me gone, _____ con - sid - er me gone, _

_____ Con - sid - er me, con - sid - er me,

Con sid - er me gone, _____ gone, _ gone, _ gone. _

Repeat and Fade

87

MOON OVER BOURBON STREET

WORDS & MUSIC BY STING

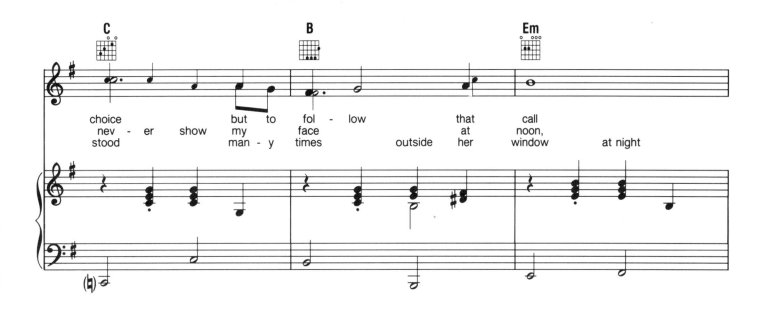

choice but to fol - low that call
nev - er show my face at noon,
stood man - y times outside her window at night

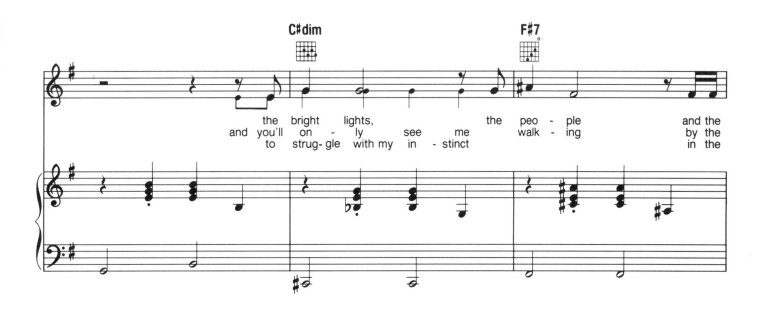

the bright lights, the peo - ple and the
and you'll on - ly see me walk - ing by the
to strug - gle with my in - stinct in the

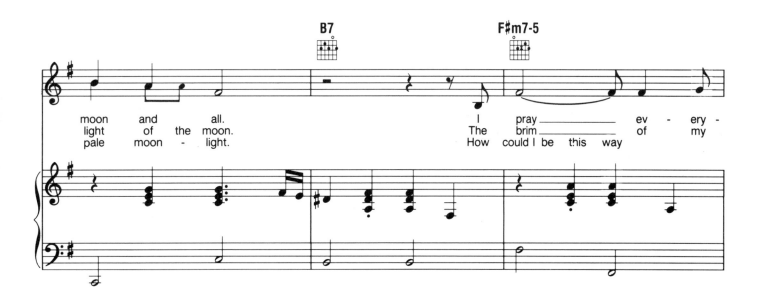

moon and all. I pray _____ ev - ery
light of the moon. The brim _____ of my
pale moon - light. How could I be this way

Bour - bon   Street.

It was

She moon o- ver

Bour - bon Street.

FORTRESS AROUND YOUR HEART

WORDS & MUSIC BY STING

To Coda ⊕

Then I____ went off to fight ___ some bat - tle ___ that I'd ___ in - vent - ed in - side
This pri - son has now be - come ___ your home, a sen - tence you seem pre - pared

____ my head. A - way so long for years ___ and years,
____ to pay. It took a day to build ___ the ci - ty.

Eb7

you pro - bab - ly thought or e - ven wished that I was dead.
We walked through its streets in the af - ter - noon, ___

96

WE'LL BE TOGETHER

WORDS & MUSIC BY STING

(1.) I see me with you and

all the things you do____ keep turn-ing round and round in my mind.____

For-get the wea -ther, we should al -ways be to -ge-ther, a - ny o - ther thought is un -

kind. To have you with me__ I would swim the se - ven seas,__ I

need you as my guide and my light.__ My love is a flame that

burns in your name,__ we'll be to - ge - ther, we'll be to - ge-ther to - night.__

VERSE 2:
I see you with me
And all I want to be
Is dancing here with you in my arms
Forget the weather
We should always be together
I'll always be a slave to your charms.

To have you with me I would swim the seven seas
I need you as my guide and my light
My love is a flame that burns in your name
We'll be together tonight.

VERSE 3:
I see you with me
And baby makes three . . .
I see me with you
And all the things we do . . .
Forget the weather we should always be together
I need you as my guide and my light
My love is a flame that burns in your name
We'll be together, we'll be together tonight.

ROCK STEADY

WORDS & MUSIC BY STING

Saw an ad._____ in the news-pa-per that caught my eye,___ I said to my ba-by this sounds like the ti-cket for you___ and I, it said vo-lun-teers want-ed for a ve-ry spe-cial trip, to com-mune __ with mo-ther na-ture on a big wood-en ship.__We took a tax-

ra - di - o, ___ it was going ___ to rain for ev - er ___ and he'd told ___ him to go, ___ "I'll pro - tect ___

___ you all don't worry, I'll be a fa - ther to you all, I'll save two of ev - 'ry a - ni - mal, no

mat - ter how small, but I'll need some as - sis - tants to look af - ter the zoo, ___ I can't see

no - bo - dy bet - ter so you'll just have to do." I said "Just tell me some - thing be - fore it's too

VERSE 2:
It rained for forty days and forty long nights
I'd never seen rain like it, it looked like our old friend was being proved right
He had no time to worry though there was just too much to do
Between the signified monkey and the kangaroo
We had to wash all the animals, we had to feed them too
We were merely human slaves in a big floating zoo
She said "Hey baby, I don't mean to be flip
But it seems this old man is on some power trip."
I said "No no sugar, you must be wrong
I mean look at the size of this boat we're on.
We're as safe as houses, as safe as mother's milk,
He's as cool as November, smooth as China silk.
He's God's best friend, he's got a seat on the board
And life may be tough but we're sailing with the Lord."

FRAGILE

WORDS & MUSIC BY STING

If blood will flow when flesh and steel are one, dry-ing in __ the col-our __ of the even-ing sun. To-mor-row's rain will wash the stains a-way, __ but some-thing in __ our minds __ will al-ways stay. __ Per -

On ____ and on ____ the rain ____ will fall ____ like

tears from _ a star, ___ like tears from _ a star ___ on ____ and on ____ the

rain ____ will say ___ how fra - gile _ we are, ___ how fra - gile _ we are. ___

Solo ad lib.

HISTORY WILL TEACH US NOTHING

WORDS & MUSIC BY STING

Medium beat

If we seek so - lace in the pri-sons of __ the dis - tant past

se - cu - ri - ty in hu-man sys - tems, we're told will al - ways, al - ways last.

E - mo-tions are the sail and blind faith is ___ the mast, ___

with-out the breath of real ___ free - dom, ___ we're get - ting no - where fast. ___

If God ___ is dead and the ac - tor plays ___ his part, ___
[*Verses 2 & 3 see under*]

116

his words of fear will find___ their way___ to a place in___ your heart.___

With-out the voice of rea - son ev - 'ry faith___ is its own curse,

with - out free-dom from___ the past things can on - ly get worse.

1, 2.

Soon - er or la - ter,___ soon- er or la - ter,___

117

Soon-er or la-ter just like the world__ first day,

soon-er or la-ter we learn to throw__the past__ a-way.__

Soon-er or la-ter just like the world__ first day,

soon-er or la-ter we learn to throw__the past__ a-way.__

Soon-er or la-ter,___ we learn to throw the past___ a-way.___

His - to - ry___ will teach us no-

thing.

His - to - ry___

will teach us no - thing.

VERSE 2:
Our written history is a catologue of crime
The sordid and the powerful, the architects of time.
The mother of invention, oppression of the mild
The constant fear of scarcity, aggression as its child.

VERSE 3:
Convince an enemy, convince him that he's wrong
To win a bloodless battle where victory is long
A simple act of faith, reason over might
To blow up his children will only prove him right.

AN ENGLISHMAN IN NEW YORK

WORDS & MUSIC BY STING

Brightly

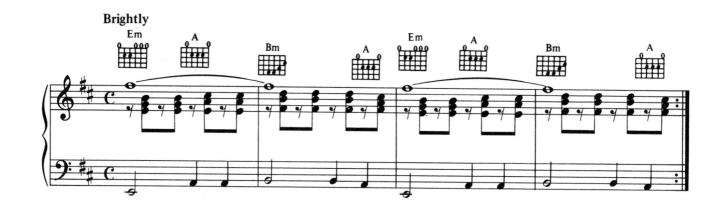

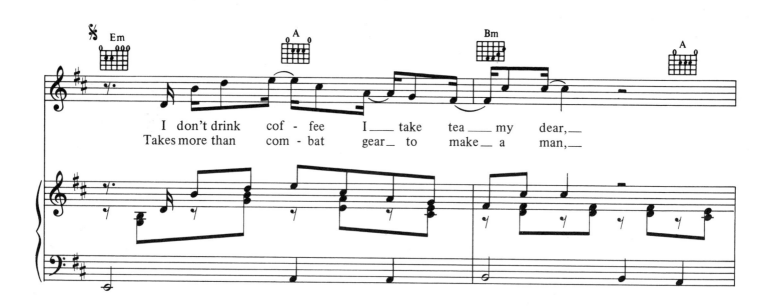

I don't drink cof-fee I ___ take tea ___ my dear, ___
Takes more than com-bat gear ___ to make ___ a man, ___

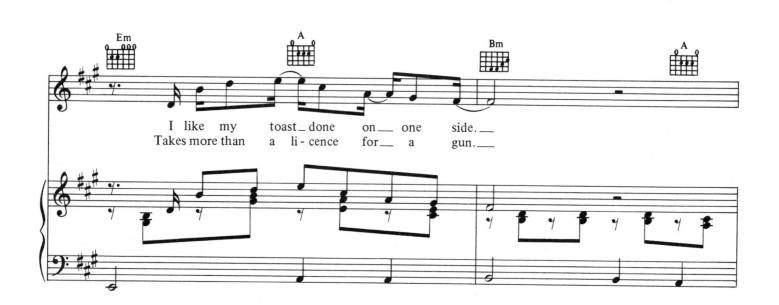

I like my toast ___ done on ___ one side. ___
Takes more than a li-cence for ___ a gun. ___

And you can   hear__ it   in__ my   ac - cent   when__ I   talk,__   I'm an
Con-front your   en - e - mies,__ a - void__ them   when__ you can, __   a

En   -   glish - man   in   New - York.____
gentle - man__ will   walk   but ne - ver   run.

(1.) You see me   walk - ing   down__ Fifth   Av - en - ue____
(2.%.) If "man-ners   mak - eth   man" as   some - one   said __

a   walk-ing   cane__ here   at__ my   side.
he's   the   he - ro   of__ the   day.

I'm an a - li - en, I'm a le - gal a - li - en, I'm an
En - glish - man in New___ York.___
Mo - des - ty___ pro - pri - e - ty,___ can
lead to no - to - ri - e - ty but you could end___ up as___ the on - ly one.___

125

Gen - tle - ness,— so - bri - e - ty, are rare in this so - ci - e - ty, at night a can-dle's bright-er than — the sun. —

Solo ad lib.

THEY DANCE ALONE

WORDS & MUSIC BY STING

(1.) Why are these wo-men here,__ danc-ing on their own?

[Verses 2 & 3 see under]

Why is there this sad - ness in their eyes?__

Why are the sol-diers here, ___ their fa - ces fixed like stone?

I can't see what it is that they ___ des - pise. ___

They're danc-ing with the miss-ing, ___ they're danc-ing with the dead, ___

they dance with the in - vi - si - ble ones, ___ their an-guish is un-said.

They're danc-ing with their fa - thers, they're danc-ing with their sons,

they're danc-ing with their hus-bands, they dance a - lone, they dance a -

lone. One day we'll dance on their graves, one day we'll sing our free - dom.

One day we'll laugh in our joy, and we'll dance.

One day we'll dance on their graves, one__ day we'll sing our free - dom.

One__ day we'll laugh in our joy, and we'll dance.__

To Coda ⊕

Ellas danzan con los desaparecidos, danzan con los muertos, danzan con amores invisíbles.

D.%. al Coda

Con silenciosa angistia, danzan con sus padres, con sus hijos, con sus esposos. Ellas danzan solos, danzan solos.

VERSE 2:
The only form of protest they're allowed
I've seen their silent faces, they scream so loud
If they were to speak these words, they'd go missing too
Another woman on the torture table, what else can they do?

VERSE 3:
Hey Mister Pinochet, you've sown a bitter crop
It's foreign money that supports you, one day the money's going to stop
No wages for your torturers, no budget for your guns
You think of your own mother dancing with her invisible son.

WHY SHOULD I CRY FOR YOU?

WORDS & MUSIC BY STING

(1.) Un - der the dog star sail __ o - ver the
(2.) Un - der the Arc - tic fire __ o - ver the
(3.) All col - ours bleed to red, __ a - sleep on the

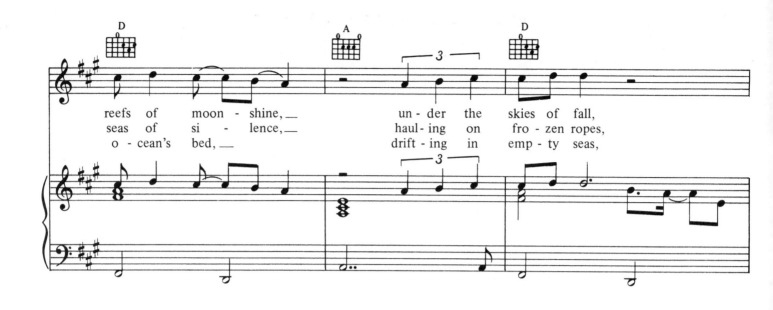

reefs of moon - shine, __ un - der the skies of fall,
seas of si - lence, __ haul - ing on fro - zen ropes,
o - cean's bed, __ drift - ing in emp - ty seas,

north - north - west, the stones of Fa - roe.
for all my days re - - main - ing.
for all my days re - - main - ing.

Would north be true?
Would north be true?
Why should I, why should I

What would be true? Why should I,

why should I cry? Why should I....

Repeat to Fade

ISLAND OF SOULS

WORDS & MUSIC BY STING

ship with no coals, they would sail to the is - land of souls.

Repeat section to Fade

Mm - bay mm- bay - day mm - bay.

Solo, over fade

ALL THIS TIME

WORDS & MUSIC BY STING

(1.) I looked out a - cross

the ri - ver to - day,

CHORUS

___ us the Ro-mans built this place, __ they built a wall and a tem-ple on the edge of the Em-pire gar-ri-son town. __ They lived and they died, __ they prayed to their gods __ but the stone gods did not make a sound, __ and their emp-_

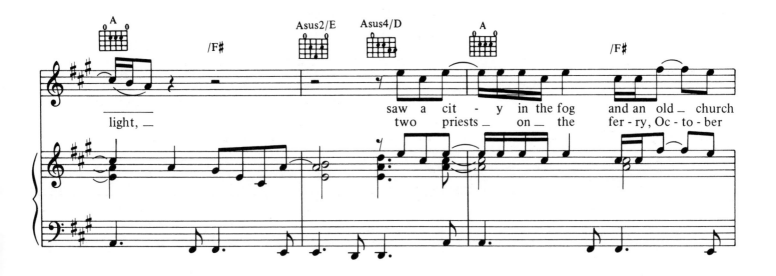

saw a cit - y in the fog and an old — church
light, — two priests — on — the fer - ry, Oc - to - ber

tow - er where the sea - gulls play. — Saw the sad —
geese on a cold win - ter's night.

VERSE 2:
Two priests came round our house tonight
One young, one old, to offer prayers for the dying
   to serve the final rite
One to learn, one to teach
Which way the cold wind blows
Fussing and flapping in priestly black
Like a murder of crows

CHORUS —

VERSE 3:
Blessed are the poor, for they shall inherit the earth
Better to be poor than a fat man in the eye of a needle
And as these words were spoken I swear I hear
The old man laughing
What good is a used up world,
And how could it be worth having

CHORUS 3:
All this time the river flowed
Endlessly like a silent tear
And all this time the river flowed
Father, if Jesus exists then how come He never lived here.

MAD ABOUT YOU

WORDS & MUSIC BY STING

though you hold the keys to ru - in of ev' - ry - thing I see, with
ev' - ry pris - on blown to dust my en - e - mies walk free, though
all my king - doms turn to sand and fall in - to the sea, I'm

mad a - bout you, I'm mad a - bout you.

WHEN THE ANGELS FALL

WORDS & MUSIC BY STING & DOMINIC MILLER

But per-haps the dream ___ is dream-ing us, ___

soar-ing with the sea-gulls.

But per-haps the dream ___ is dream-ing us, ___

a - stride ___ the backs ___ of ___ ea - gles.

When the an - gels fall. ____

These are my feet, these are my hands,

these are my child-ren, this is my __ de-mand.

Bring down the an - gels, cast them from __ my sight,

VERSE 2:
Take your father's cross
Gently from the wall
A shadow still remaining
See the churches fall
In mighty arcs of sound
And all that they're containing
Yet all the ragged souls
Of all the ragged men
Looking for their lost homes
Shuffle to the ruins
From the levelled plain
To search among the tombstones.

THE SOUL CAGES

WORDS & MUSIC BY STING

(1.) The boy child is locked in the fish-er-man's yard,

there's a bloodless moon where the o-ceans die.__ A shoal of night stars hang__

fire in the nest __ and the cha-os of ca-ges __ where the cray-fish lie.__

(3.) He's the king of the ninth — world,

the twist-ed son of the fog — bells' — toll.   In — each — and ev - 'ry lob-

- ster cage, — a tor - tured hu - man soul.

(4.) I have a wa-ger, the brave __ child spoke, __ the fish - er-man laughed, though dis - turbed __

__ at the joke. __ You will drink __ what I drink __ but you must __

__ e -qual me __ and if the drink leaves me stand-ing, __ a soul __ shall go free. (5.) I
[(6.) And what's]

__ with me. __ These are the soul __ ca - ges

ca - ges,   these are the soul ___ ca - ges.

And he dreamed ___ of a ship ___ on the sea, ___

___ it would car - ry his fa - ther and me   to a place ___

___ they could ne - ver be found ___   to a place ___

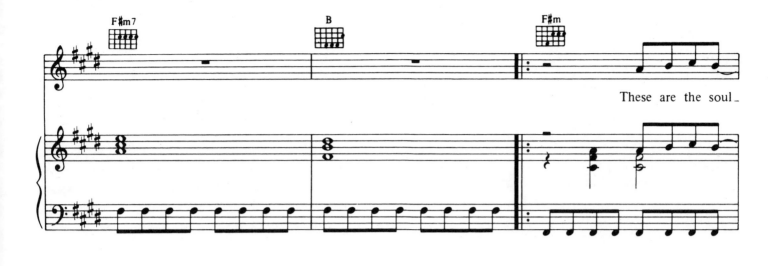

These are the soul—

_____ ca - ges,   these are the soul _____ ca - ges.

A

VERSE 2:

Where is the fisherman, where is the goat
Where is the keeper in his carrion coat?
Eclipse on the moon when the dark bird flies
Where is the child with his father's eyes?

B

VERSE 5:

I have here a cask of most magical wine
A vintage that blessed every ship in the line
It's wrung from the blood of the sailors who died
Young white bodies adrift in the tide.

VERSE 6:

And what's in it for me my pretty young thing
Why should I whistle when the caged bird sings
If you lose a wager with the king of the sea
You'll spend the rest of forever in the cage with me.

VERSE 7:

A body lies open in the fisherman's yard
Like the side of a ship where the iceberg rips
One less soul in the soul cages
One last curse on the fisherman's lips.

9/93(16061)